PRAISE FOR THE BINGE CURE METHOD

"The Binge Cure Journal is a perfect solution for anyone looking to understand and mend their relationship with food. Dr. Nina's straightforward and empathetic approach offers insight into how our issues with food are often about much more than what's on our plate. This loving and graceful tool has the power to help people change their lives. Thank you, Dr. Nina!"

—*Jodi Harrison Bauer, host of the Fearlessly Authentic podcast*

"Dieting—as much fun as being covered in honey and chased by bears. Struggling with binge eating—similar to dieting, but trying to lick the honey off yourself while running is much harder. The Binge Cure is a beacon of insight and clarity in a landscape of dietary tribalism. While the diet industry encourages us to deny and repress our human experience in favor of creating transactional, mathematical, and dysfunctional relationships with food, Dr. Nina Savelle-Rocklin challenges the concept of food addiction, speaks out against the prohibition of feeling in modern society, and provides a pathway out of binge eating paved with self-awareness."

—*Marcus Kain, nutrition coach, host of the Strong Not Starving podcast*

"As a seasoned psychoanalyst with great experience in these matters, Dr. Savelle-Rocklin enables readers to understand, and master, the real causes of their compulsive eating. By looking beyond the surface of what you eat to why you eat, she brings clarity to this very misunderstood area."

—*Lance Dodes, MD, assistant clinical professor of psychiatry (retired), Harvard Medical School; author of* **The Heart of Addiction, Breaking Addiction,** *and* **The Sober Truth**

"The Binge Cure outlines practical tips and techniques to make peace with food and your body. Dr. Nina Savelle-Rocklin is a renowned expert on the issue and provides critical insight to overcome emotional overeating, stop dieting, and live the physically and emotionally healthy life that you deserve!"

—*Jacquelyn Ekern, MS, LPC, president at Weight Hope, Addiction Hope, and Eating Disorder Hope*

PRAISE FOR THE BINGE CURE METHOD

"Listeners to Dr. Nina's weekly program on L.A. Talk Radio know that she focuses on what's eating 'at' you instead of on what you're eating. In this book she brings wisdom, knowledge, and compassion to help readers understand and change their emotional eating habits. The Binge Cure is a must-read for anyone who craves a healthier, happier relationship to themselves."

—*Craig Ramsay,* celebrity trainer and fitness expert, *author of* **Anatomy of Stretching**

"Dr. Nina hits an emotional bull's-eye zeroing in on the unmistakable truth behind the reality of binge eating and its successful treatment in The Binge Cure. This game-changing book provides a road map to assist readers in identifying the pain that fuels the fury of so-called food addiction and learning to recognize the relationship between the foods one reaches for and the circumstances under which they're reaching. Full of exercises that accompany case examples of patients from her thriving private practice—patients who have achieved success utilizing her methods—Dr. Nina provides a much-needed solution to the epidemic of eating disorders that are consuming society. Brilliantly written with the compassionate voice of someone who has triumphed in the battlefield herself, The Binge Cure provides the truth of why diets will never work and arms the reader with the knowledge necessary to successfully navigate that pain and rise above it."

—*Kelley Gunter,* author of **You Have Such a Pretty Face**

"This book is THE BIBLE on how to pry yourself off the scale and out of the never-ending cycle of yo-yo dieting, food obsession, and confusing your life goals with your weight goals. Dr. Nina tackles the tough questions and the complicated issues surrounding food, emotional eating, and physical well-being. And her solutions are sensible and based on real case studies, her guidance indispensable. This book is a keeper."

—*Iris Ruth Pastor,* author of **The Secret Life of a Weight-Obsessed Woman: Wisdom to Live the Life You Crave**

THE
BINGE CURE
JOURNAL

A GUIDE TO LIBERATING YOURSELF
FROM EMOTIONAL EATING:
TAKING CONTROL OF YOUR LIFE
AND FEELING GOOD IN YOUR BODY

by

Dr. Nina Savelle-Rocklin

ADLER PRESS
Published by Adler Press
Calabasas, California

@2023 Dr. Nina Savelle-Rocklin

Design by Kelly Bartell
Cover by Kelly Bartell

ISBN 978-1-7339946-6-8 (paperback)
ISBN 978-1-7339946-7-5 (e-book)

The material in this book is intended to provide accurate and authoritative information but should not be used as a substitute for professional care. The author and publisher urge you to consult with a mental health care provider or seek other professional advice in the event that you require expert assistance.

CONTENTS

FOREWORD

By Nikki Sharp, best-selling author of "The 5-Day Real Food Detox" and
"Meal Prep Your Way to Weight Loss. Host of A Sharper Life podcast.

I came across Dr. Nina Savelle-Rocklin on Instagram and was immediately enthralled by the depth of her content and all she teaches. At the time, I was not yet aware how similar our stories were, or that we'd one day end up going on each other's podcasts to promote messages of hope and healing.

When looking at someone's social media profiles, we tend not to get the full scope of what has led them into their respective field or why they are passionate about what they do. It's only after we decide to subscribe, follow, or join their community that we learn their teaching style and what I believe is the most important piece: their WHY.

I can say with certainty that Dr. Nina's "why" behind becoming a psychoanalyst and helping others is a story of tremendous courage and inspiration. Like me, she suffered eating disorders that took over every aspect of her life. If you are in possession of this journal, I can ascertain you too have had, or currently experience some level of suffering when it comes to the relationship with food and your body.

From getting to know Dr. Nina, including reading her books, interviewing her on my own podcast A Sharper Life, and being a guest two times on her respective shows, I am in awe of the level of integrity and depth she shares. While we both healed ourselves and have gone on to teach others our methodologies, Dr. Nina is not only an inspiration for me, but everyone who comes across her content.

Speaking from experience, I know first-hand how hard it is to feel alone and hopeless. I understand the frustration you have when thinking about food and wanting to change your body. I also know the pain that comes from bingeing, restricting, and feeling like you'll never see the results you want. To feel at peace with yourself and the relationship you have with something we all must have every day.

Dr. Nina's unique methodology and commitment to others, and her development of The Binge Cure Method is inspiring. While we speak a similar language when it comes to our teachings, Dr. Nina has the backing of decades of research and proven strategies.

I commend you, the reader, for picking up a copy of the Binge Cure Journal as you are taking your healing to the next level. As you read and go through the prompts, keep in mind that you can overcome whatever challenge you are facing and find freedom.

—Nikki Sharp

WELCOME

I'm so glad you're here! Let me ask you something:

How often do you lose control over food? Maybe you wake up every morning with the best intentions. You vow to be "good" and stick to your diet. Over the next several days or weeks, you eat right, go to the gym, and drop a few pounds. Maybe you get your hopes up that this is finally it. You dream of slipping on a pair of skinny jeans, imagining them sliding over your hips with ease.

Before you know it, you fall off the diet wagon by eating one of your forbidden foods. To cope with the feelings of guilt, you polish off the rest of that dessert, pizza, a bag of chips, or whatever is in the fridge. When it's time to get back on track, there are so many choices: Weight Watchers, Paleo, Whole30, South Beach, Mediterranean, low carb, high carb, liquid, cookie diet, and ketogenic. You start another diet, only to get derailed again and gain back the weight you just lost.

Maybe you also try counting steps as well as macros, but you just wind up with a really cool Fitbit and zero sustainable change on the bathroom scale. So there you are with two different sets of clothes in your closet—one for the size you are and one for the size you want to be. You're more than ready for something new, but you don't know what to do instead of dieting. You're afraid that if you're not on some kind of diet, you're going to pack on the pounds. You're afraid you're always going to look like a "before" photo. That fit, slim "after" photo seems like an impossible dream.

Maybe you feel as if you're addicted to food, especially when you feel that irresistible, unstoppable urge to head into the kitchen. Or perhaps you know exactly why you're eating, but you don't know how to change the control that food has over you. You want to eat normally, and you want to feel normal, but you don't know how to get there.

That's why I created this journal. In the following pages, you'll find powerful prompts and guided exercises to help you achieve all of your goals.

That's why I created this journal. In the following pages, you'll find powerful prompts and guided exercises to help you achieve all of your goals. You'll start creating a life free from binge eating. You'll be able to stop food obsession, guilt, and body shame, so you can experience food freedom and enjoy a more relaxed and compassionate way of being in the world.

In this guided journal, I'm going to show you exactly how to stop bingeing so you can experience a healthy relationship with food and your body. No dieting necessary. Not only will you finally be able to fit into those skinny jeans in the back of your closet, but you'll also break free from the preoccupation with food and eating. For so many dieters, the goal isn't just changing the number on the scale. They want to stop their obsession with food, to stop thinking about every bite.

As a psychoanalyst specializing in eating disorders, I'm here to help you navigate a path to lasting health without counting calories, fat grams, or carbs. You may wonder what exactly a psychoanalyst does and how that differs from other kinds of therapy. One of my patients said it best: "Therapy is like snorkeling. You go a little under the surface and see some cool things. But analysis? That's like deep sea diving to the bottom of the ocean. It's pitch black, and you've got to shine a light in the darkness to see what's down there."

Shining that light helps you discover the hidden reasons you're turning to food. In my private clinical practice and through my online programs, I've helped thousands of people all over the world heal their relationship with food, stop bingeing, lose those extra pounds, and gain health. In the following pages, I share powerful prompts, exercises, and questions designed to help you create the food freedom you crave. We'll illuminate the hidden beliefs that are keeping you stuck and start cultivating new ways of relating to yourself, the world, and, of course, food.

Imagine what it will be like to wake up and think about your day, not your diet. Think of how it will feel to escape food obsession, body shame, and guilt and create a life of liberation, peace, and self-love. I'm confident that as you go through this journal, you'll deconstruct old ideas and construct new ones, creating more freedom every day. By the time you reach the last page, your life will be different. I'm excited for you!

Let's get started.

HOW THIS BOOK WORKS:

A message of hope.

I'll never forget the woman who called into my radio program and confessed to eating cookies. She described herself as being "in recovery" from bingeing and was keeping a food journal, tracking every bite. She used a combination of willpower and accountability to stay on track, but inevitably, she got derailed and ended up eating her favorite guilty pleasure—cookies.

"I'll have to deal with this for the rest of my life," she said. "Being in recovery takes commitment."

That's when I told her I didn't believe in recovery.

There was stunned silence on the line (which is not ideal for a live radio program). I quickly clarified. **"I believe in liberation."**

Why don't I believe in recovery? The way I see it, we recover from disappointment or a nasty breakup. We recover from an injury or sickness. We recover from a financial setback. Being "in" recovery means being stuck there, always thinking about food, trying to "be good" and focusing on what not to eat.

We don't say we're "in recovery" from depression. We might explain that we were depressed and now we feel better. Similarly, we don't say we're "in recovery" from anxiety. We say that we once struggled with anxiety, but not anymore.

For binge eating, stress eating, or any kind of emotional eating, we don't recover. We liberate ourselves. Liberation means freedom from counting calories. It's freedom from the idea that you're good if you eat healthy foods and bad if you eat something with a carb. Freedom from obsession, guilt, and shame.

Liberation is all of those things and more. What does your liberated life look like? It might be…

The freedom of not thinking about food all the time

Being able to wear anything in your closet

Shopping in any store you want and wearing outfits you like, instead of picking clothes to hide your body

Never giving a thought to what others think of your food choices in a restaurant or the grocery store

Ordering whatever you want at restaurants without a second thought

Eating in front of people with confidence

Listening to your body and easily eating intuitively

Each of the prompts, questions, and guided exercises in this journal helps you dig deeper into the hidden reasons behind bingeing and find new ways to deal with them so you can find food freedom once and for all. These prompts correspond to one of the following themes and categories:

 The Diet Buster Prompts: It's time to take your power back from the mirror and the bathroom scale. An inanimate piece of metal and plastic can't measure your true value, and a mirror shouldn't have that much impact on your self-esteem. These questions help you ditch dieting forever.

 The Food-Mood Formula Secrets: Food may seem like the trigger, but it's not. To stop bingeing forever, it's essential to crack the code of emotional eating and discover the hidden emotions and situations that are the real triggers. We're not actually triggered by food, even though it seems as if we are. Situations and emotions that are often hidden and out of awareness are the true culprits behind bingeing. These prompts shine a light in our hidden minds to illuminate the truth.

 The Self-Love Activators: Is your inner critic louder than it should be? If you're judgmental and harsh toward yourself, you might turn to food just to escape your own mean voice. These prompts and questions help you convert that inner critic into a friend.

 The Food Freedom Identifiers: Let's journey into the past, but not to blame or point fingers. Instead, these prompts show you how the past continues to influence your present-day conflicts and challenges. Once you identify and resolve those emotional wounds, you can create a path to food freedom.

 Self-Care Mastery Prescriptions: Self-care goes beyond workouts, mani-pedis, massages, and facials. It's vital to discover new ways to respond to yourself, other people, and the world. You can't hate yourself into feeling good about yourself. These prompts help you turn insecurities into self-confidence.

 Stop-the-Sabotage Clarifiers: If you've ever lost weight and then found yourself sabotaging your progress, you're not alone. We often hide the reasons for sabotage deep in our minds. These prompts highlight and resolve those conflicts, so when you start losing weight, you'll stay on track. That's when the weight comes off naturally and remains off.

 The Dream Life Roadmap: These questions help you stay in the present without anxiety about the future so that you can enjoy a balanced, peaceful, and happy life.

Keep in mind, with binge eating, stress eating, or any kind of emotional eating, the real problem is not what you're eating, it's what's eating "at" you. This journal gives you everything you need to figure that out and create change instead of focusing on "what" you're eating. You'll discover new strategies to express your emotions, needs, and wants. And you'll learn new ways of responding to yourself. When we accept ourselves, our emotions, our weirdness, our nderfulness and learn to be nice to ourselves, then we break free from bingeing for good. By making peace with ourselves, we make peace with food, too.

That means not thinking about food every minute of the day. Being able to stay out of the kitchen at night. Not judging ourselves. Nobody is perfect, and that's what makes life interesting. It means having a more relaxed and compassionate way of being in the world.

A client in my online program wrote to say, "Thank you for freeing me from 40 years of dieting and living on low-fat foods and sugar-free this and that."

She told me she was in Paris and enjoying some tasty French food, with no inner critic bullying her. She said, "Here's to being free and living life to the max!"

Now that's freedom! If you want the same liberation, get started on the prompts, exercises, and guidance in this journal so you can enjoy your binge-free, happy life.

THE DIET BUSTER PROMPTS

"Never trust a four-letter word where the first three letters spell die."
Taryn Brumfitt, **Embrace** documentary

The diet industry is a $60 billion per year industry and business is booming. According to the CDC, nearly half of all Americans are on a diet. That's 162 million dieters. The UK has 13 million dieters. Australia has nearly 3 million dieters. And that's just a few countries. One study found that by the time the average woman is 45 years old, been on 61 different diets.

Dieting always involves some kind of deprivation, and the anticipation or experience of deprivation leads to wanting what you can't have. You end up bingeing on all the foods that are off-limits. By giving up the diet habit, you can say goodbye to binge eating, body shame, and diets that don't work.

Imagine being able to keep any food in the house without bingeing on it. Think about what it would be like to stop bingeing, lose weight, to be fitter and healthier, and happier in your life. It is possible. And, when you stop dieting, you take your power back from food and get your life back.

If you're ready to stop dieting and discover food freedom, it's time to take your power back from the mirror and the bathroom scale.

If you're ready to stop dieting and discover food freedom, it's time to take your power back from the mirror and the bathroom scale. An inanimate piece of metal and plastic can't measure your true value. It really is possible to break free from the endless cycle of dieting and finally develop a healthy relationship with food. The first step is to ditch the diet mentality once and for all. Say goodbye to dieting and take the first step toward a healthier and happier life.

WHAT'S YOUR DIET COUNT?

Make a list of all the diets you've been on.

How long did you stay on each of them?

THE DIET BUSTER PROMPT: WHAT'S YOUR DIET COUNT?

What was it like to be on a diet?

THE DIET BUSTER PROMPT: WHAT'S YOUR DIET COUNT?

What happened when you went off the diet?

THE DIET BUSTER PROMPT

LAST SUPPER MENTALITY

The "last supper mentality" means eating everything on your "bad foods" list before starting a new diet. It's like you're having your "last supper" before embarking on a restrictive diet. Many people eat all their favorite foods or indulge in everything they've been craving before they start a diet, as if they won't be able to have those foods again. The anticipation of deprivation only makes you want something more, which leads to overeating or bingeing, and then feeling guilty.

How do you relate to this?

THE DIET BUSTER PROMPT: LAST SUPPER MENTALITY

Describe your typical "last supper" meal or food choices.

Why is this food usually off-limits?

THE DIET BUSTER PROMPT

HUNGER SCALE

On a scale of 1-5, with 5 being ravenous and 1 being slightly hungry, where are you right now?

1   2   3   4   5

What do you associate with hunger?

THE DIET BUSTER PROMPT: HUNGER SCALE

When you think about hunger, what does it actually feel like in your body?
How does it physically show up for you?

THE DIET BUSTER PROMPT: HUNGER SCALE

What does it mean to you to be hungry?

THE DIET BUSTER PROMPT: HUNGER SCALE

What memories do you have about being deprived of food or rewarded with food?

OVEREATING VS. BINGEING

Overeating means "eating to excess" and that's different from bingeing. There are lots of reasons for overeating that don't always have to do with emotions. Many Americans overeat on Thanksgiving, which one of my patients cleverly referred to as "National Binge Day."

Overeating on that holiday often has to do with food, not feelings.

If you don't eat enough and you get to where you're ravenous, you may overeat. If that's the case, you might think, "Oh, I overdid it, so I'll cut back tomorrow."

Bingeing⊠ means eating large quantities of food at one time, in a compulsive way, often without enjoying it or even tasting it. Bingeing is a way of coping with something inside. It's about using food for comfort, distraction, or to numb or express pain, anger, anxiety, or anything uncomfortable.

Unlike overeating, bingeing means being out of control with food and usually involves remorse, guilt, and shame afterward.

Afterward, you might think, "What's wrong with me?" Not only do you feel bad about what you ate but also you feel terrible about yourself.

What do you tell yourself when you overeat?

THE DIET BUSTER PROMPT: OVEREATING VS. BINGEING

What are your thoughts about yourself when you binge?

PHYSICAL VS. EMOTIONAL HUNGER

Let's distinguish between physical and emotional hunger. Here are some signs that you're physically hungry:

Growling, gurgling stomach | Feeling light-headed
Getting a headache (especially if you haven't eaten for some hours)

In contrast, the signs that you're emotionally hungry are located more in your thoughts and your mind than in your body:

A specific food "sounds good" or "looks good."
You want to reward yourself | You want to calm down or feel better.

Many people eat to feel more energized, which isn't emotional hunger, but it's not the best response to exhaustion. When you're tired, you need to rest. Food won't perk you up for long. Your body needs rest, not food.

Think about the last time you felt out of control with food. Were you physically hungry?   Y E S / N O

If not, what was going on in your life?

THE DIET BUSTER PROMPT

SURF THE HUNGER WAVE

When you're not sure whether it's emotional or physical hunger, try postponing your meal or snack for three minutes and see what happens. If you're physically hungry, you'll probably get hungrier, but not so ravenous that you lose control. If you're emotionally hungry, you may become more aware of the underlying emotions that are the driving force behind the urge to eat.

If that happens, it's time to go surfing. Yes, surfing. No surfboard or ocean required. When that urge to binge or to continue eating strikes—and it can be powerful—imagine that you're surfing the feeling.

A wave builds up intensity and becomes more and more powerful, and then it eventually crashes and disappears. Same thing with a binge. It can build up and feel super intense. But it won't stay that intense. It will crest and then diminish in intensity.

That's something to keep in mind when you want to eat for emotional reasons. The craving or urge will not last. If you can ride the wave for a little while, it will eventually pass. When you know whether you're hungry for food or eating to resolve an internal conflict or state, it's easier to make healthy food choices.

Three minutes may not sound like a long time, but it can make a big difference.

Try it and write about your experience.

THE DIET BUSTER PROMPT: SURF THE HUNGER WAVE

What did you notice?

What surprised you?

THE DIET BUSTER PROMPT

LET'S LOOK AT HOW DIETING HAS IMPACTED YOUR LIFE

Diet culture mentality is everywhere. Maybe you constantly count calories or feel guilty for indulging in your favorite foods, or any food that's not on your "allowed" list of safe food.

This can leave you feeling frustrated and anxious, and it can affect your self-esteem and even your relationships. To move toward a healthier and more balanced relationship with food, consider the negative consequences of dieting in your life.

What has dieting deprived you of?

THE DIET BUSTER PROMPT: LET'S LOOK AT HOW DIETING HAS IMPACTED YOUR LIFE

If you weren't dieting, what would meals with friends be like?

What aspects of life would be more enjoyable?

CULTIVATE RAINBOW THINKING

Have you ever caught yourself thinking in extremes? Like something is either amazing or terrible, with no middle ground? For example, you might think you ruined the whole day by eating cake.
Black and white thinking makes you feel stuck and hopeless when things don't go as planned. Here are some examples:

I'm always going to struggle with food | I'm never going to get over this
I have to be perfect | I'm such a failure at losing weight

The good news is that between black and white is a world of COLOR!

I'm learning a new way of eating | I'm creating a new relationship with food
I'm doing the best that I can | It takes time to create change | It's okay to eat ice cream sometimes

Which of the black-and-white beliefs resonate with you?   *What is an alternative belief?*

THE DIET BUSTER PROMPT

IS IT YUMMY?

My one food rule is that whatever I eat has to be delicious. It has to be yummy. Think about how many blah meals you've eaten because it's on your diet. Eventually, you just want something that tastes good. And then, chances are that all bets are off.

*Take a moment and forget what you think you should or shouldn't eat (aka diet mentality). What do you actually **like** to eat?*

THE DIET BUSTER PROMPT: IS IT YUMMY?

Make a list of forbidden foods

Give yourself permission to have something from the forbidden list.

Eat it mindfully. Put it on a plate or in a bowl. Take your time and enjoy each bite. Allow yourself the pleasure of that food. Then, describe your experience.

Was the food as good as you thought it would be?

THE DIET BUSTER PROMPT: IS IT YUMMY?

How satisfying was this experience of eating in this way?

What were the difficulties?

THE FOOD-MOOD FORMULA SECRETS

Take a moment to think about your last craving. Did you want something smooth like ice cream? Or filling like pizza or cake? Or maybe you grabbed that last bag of chips.

What does it all mean?

In my first decade working with patients, I started noticing that their go-to binge foods had everything to do with their hidden emotional conflicts. I realized that when they were bingeing, what they chose to eat **in that moment** was directly related to the hidden WHY they were bingeing.

...what they chose to eat **in that moment** *was directly related to the hidden WHY they were bingeing.*

Write down your last craving: what food did you want?

What foods are irresistible? Or off-limits? Why?

THE CREAMY SECRET

When we crave ice cream or something creamy, it isn't ice cream we really want—it's comfort. The key to change is finding new ways to comfort ourselves that don't involve eating.

Where in your life do you need comfort?

THE FILLING SECRET

Filling food takes up space within and is related to symbolically filling a void.
Instead, let's look at the holes in your life, the empty spaces, and find new ways
to fill them. Take a moment to think about what is missing from your life.

What do you need more of?

What is missing in your life?

THE CRUNCHY SECRET

Anything that makes us bite down hard is associated with forms
of anger, like frustration or annoyance, irritation, rage. Instead,
learn to express anger in a healthier way—with words.

What is causing you frustration, irritation, annoyance, resentment or anger?
(remember: do NOT turn that anger against yourself)

THE CHOCOLATE SECRET

Some of us only like milk chocolate or chocolate with creamy centers. Others won't eat chocolate without nuts. Plain dark chocolate usually has a bit of a crunch. So, chocolate is creamy, associated with comfort, or it's crunchy, associated with forms of anger.

How does this relate to your life?

THE SWEETNESS IDENTIFIER

Also, maybe you need more *sweetness* in your life. Not the kind that comes from sugar, but the sweetness of connection, fulfillment, and love.

What comes to mind?

THE FOOD-MOOD FORMULA SECRETS

The Food-Mood Formula is a tool that helps you discover your hidden WHY... so you can focus on what's eating "at" you instead of on what you're eating. Next time you get a craving, consider if it's creamy, filling, or crunchy. When you identify and respond to those underlying needs, emotions, wishes, and conflicts, you stop eating to cope.

Keep in mind that enjoying some chips with your sandwich is not the same as eating a family-size bag and hating yourself with every bite.

The Food-Mood Formula only applies to situations when you feel a pull towards food to change the way you emotionally feel.

Express Yourself

As you can see, what you're eating isn't even the real problem. Let's talk about the real problem: We live in a society that says it's not okay to have emotions. We're considered weak if we have them and strong if we push them away. The message is, there's something wrong with our basic human emotions, which connect us to ourselves and to each other.

Scared? Be strong! Fight! Don't give in to fear!

Angry? You're an angry person. You need anger management classes.

Sad? You must be depressed; take an antidepressant.

Anxious? There's a pill for that, too.

The message is, there's something wrong with emotions.

And of course, many of us do benefit from medication. I'm referring to injunctions against our basic, human emotions, which connect us to ourselves and to each other.

With all these prohibitions, it's no wonder so many of us don't know how to comfort ourselves, be with ourselves, express ourselves, or respond to ourselves.

No wonder so many of us eat as a way of coping. Yet, when we find other ways of coping, everything changes.

Once you use the Food-Mood Formula to identify what the true emotions, wishes, conflicts, or needs are, the next step is to express them in words. After all, the only way to get rid of feelings is to feel them.

Keep in mind, we don't express our emotions to change the situation. We express ourselves to change the way we feel about a situation.

GIVE ANGER A VOICE

I'm exasperated (because/when/that)...
(e.g., "I'm exasperated when I ask people to clean up after themselves and they don't do it.")

I'm annoyed...

I'm frustrated...

I resent...

I'm angry...

I'm furious...

GIVE SADNESS A VOICE

I'm feeling down (because/when/that)...
(e.g., "I'm feeling down because I got a bad review at my job.")

I'm unhappy...

I'm hurt...

I'm sad...

I'm dejected...

I'm depressed...

GIVE ANXIETY A VOICE

I'm concerned (because/when/that)...
(e.g., "I'm concerned because I have a huge presentation to give at work.")

I'm uneasy...

I'm worried...

I'm afraid...

I'm terrified...

GIVE GUILT A VOICE

I'm apologetic (because/when/that)...
(e.g., "I'm apologetic because I worked late again and missed dinner with my family.")

I'm contrite...

I'm regretful...

I'm remorseful...

GIVE SHAME A VOICE

I'm embarrassed . . .
(e.g., "I'm embarrassed that I ate an entire pizza by myself.")

I feel awkward about/when . . .

I'm humiliated . . .

I'm feeling degraded . . .

I'm mortified . . .

GIVE LONELINESS A VOICE

I'm feeling empty (because/when/that)...
(e.g., "I feel empty when my family doesn't visit me.")

I'm feeling alone...

I'm feeling isolated...

I'm feeling abandoned...

I'm feeling rejected...

GIVE HELPLESSNESS A VOICE

I'm dependent (because/when/that) . . .
(e.g., "I'm dependent because I rely on my parents to pay my bills.")

I'm defenseless . . .

I'm powerless . . .

I'm weak . . .

I'm vulnerable . . .

TRACK YOUR TRIGGERS

Situation: *What happened?*
Where were you? e.g., I worked all day, cooked dinner, and nobody helped to clean up afterwards

Emotions: *What were you feeling?*
Hurt, sad, angry, happy, fearful, anxious, etc.

Rate the intensity of your emotions on a scale of 1—10 *(10 is the most intense)*
e.g., I felt frustrated, upset, and hurt. (a 5 on the scale of 1—10)

Thoughts: *What does it mean?*
For example, "It means that my time is not important to my family and my needs don't matter."

Foods: *What did you turn to?*
Using the Food-Mood Formula, identify the emotions associated with those foods. For example, I ate chips and then ice cream. I felt frustrated and I needed comfort.

HOW TO COMFORT YOURSELF

Here's a formula to comfort yourself with words.

Validate: Recognize that your feelings and thoughts are reactions to a particular situation, and you have an absolute right to feel the way you feel. ie: I got passed over for a promotion at work and my co-worker got it instead. I feel hurt, unappreciated and upset. Of course I feel that way. How else could I feel given this situation?

Acknowledge: Accept the existence and truth of what you're feeling. e.g., This is a painful, upsetting, and humiliating situation. I also realize that some of my sibling issues might have gotten stirred up, since my brother was always getting special treatment.

Reassure: Encourage and inspire yourself by remembering that this situation will pass, and you will feel better. Keep in mind past situations in which you were able to overcome difficulty. You will this time, too! e.g., I've overcome a lot of challenges in my life (recall them specifically) and I'm going to get past this, too. I feel awful now, but I'm not going to be stuck in this horrible feeling. I will feel better.

Yourself! (that's you)

Give it a try. Think of a situation where you need some comfort and support:

Validate:

Acknowledge:

Reassure:

Yourself!

BODY TALK

Take a moment to consider these statements:

I feel fat.
I ate so much my stomach hurts.
My clothes are uncomfortable.
Just thinking about that gives me a headache.

Each of these sentences has a surface meaning. Yet when we dig a little deeper, we discover a hidden communication. Just as the type of food you choose can offer clues about your inner world, so can your body language. So let's start translating!

Hint: Even if you don't have the physical sensation referenced in the first part of each sentence, answer the second question.

Does your stomach hurt?
What is hurting your feelings?

Do you have a headache?
What is painful to think about?

Does your neck hurt?
What burdens are you shouldering?

Are you always hungry?
What do you want more of?

Do you feel uncomfortably full or have some discomfort in your body?
What is emotionally uncomfortable and causing you discomfort?

Do you feel pressure in your body?
What pressure are you experiencing in your life?

When you translate your "body language" into emotions, needs, and wants, you can meet those needs with words, experiences and relationships instead of with food.

THE SELF-LOVE ACTIVATORS

There's something powerful about learning to love and accept ourselves. Think of self-love as a magical key that opens up so many doors in life. When you truly start embracing who you are and being kind to yourself, it changes the way you approach relationships, handle challenges, and even how you see the world.

Giving yourself permission to be your own best friend, cheering yourself on, and celebrating your victories makes life better. It makes a huge difference in your life—and in your relationship with food.

Giving yourself permission to be your own best friend, cheering yourself on, and celebrating your victories makes life better.

DRAW A SELF-PORTRAIT (OR TWO)

Unlike the zone experienced during a binge, a creative flow is a positive experience that helps us connect to our truest inner selves. So, it's time to get in touch with your creativity.

First, draw the self you show to the world.

THE SELF-LOVE ACTIVATORS: DRAW A SELF-PORTRAIT (OR TWO)

Then, draw the secret self you don't show anyone.

What's the disconnect between the two parts?

What are the parts of yourself that you hide from other people?

THE SELF-LOVE ACTIVATORS: DRAW A SELF-PORTRAIT (OR TWO)

What would happen if people could see and know both sides of you?

Don't worry about being a good artist. The purpose of this exercise is to get
in touch with the parts of you that you keep hidden, even from yourself.

INSPIRE YOURSELF: STEP ONE

Think about three things that you are proud of accomplishing in your life. For example:

Getting married | Raising children | Leaving a bad relationship

Traveling somewhere new | Achieving a promotion | Completing a difficult project

Having a group of friends | Earning a degree | Moving to a new place

Don't justify the merit of these accomplishments.

Just write them down.

INSPIRE YOURSELF: STEP TWO

Now, think about the positive qualities it takes to achieve those things:

« Getting married means **being vulnerable, trusting, making a commitment**

« Raising children involves putting the well-being others before yourself and being a **caring** person

« Leaving a bad relationship is an act of **courage** — lots of people are too scared to leave bad relationships out of fear

« Traveling means you are **adventurous**

« Getting promoted or completing a difficult project means that you are **hard-working** and **tenacious**

« Having a group of friends means you're **likable** and **lovable**

« Earning a degree takes **dedication** and **perseverance**

List your positive qualities.

IMAGINE THE OUTCOME

If it's difficult to take a step towards a goal, then think about how you will feel, think and act when you're done.

If you're having a tough time tolerating upsetting emotions and you find yourself drawn to food, imagine how you'll feel when you work through those emotions without coping with food.

REWARD YOURSELF

Think of something you really, really want. Something tangible, or specific, like a new pair of shoes, tickets to a concert or a play, or a vacation day.

Then, promise yourself that when you accomplish your goal (whatever it is) that will be your reward.

List the ways you will reward and inspire yourself:

DESCRIBE YOURSELF

How would your best friend describe you? Describe yourself from the perspective of people who know and like you—or even better, people who love you. When you see yourself through loving, accepting eyes, when you're "sweeter" to yourself, your self-esteem improves and you feel good.

When you acknowledge who you are as a person, instead of focusing on what you weigh, you will gain a new appreciation for yourself! Describe yourself today, and celebrate who you are!

Today's action is to describe your qualities—use this list as a guide!

Achiever	Entrepreneurial	Kind	Reliable
Accepting	Flexible	Knowledgeable	Resourceful
Accomplished	Focused	Literate	Respectful
Adaptable	Enthusiastic	Logical	Responsible
Analytical	Facilitator	Loving	Self-reliant
Articulate	Friendly	Loyal	Sensible
Artistic	Fun	Mature	Sensitive
Assertive	Funny	Meditative	Sincere
Attentive	Generous	Methodical	Sociable
Communicative	Genuine	Modest	Sophisticated
Compassionate	Grateful	Motivated	Tactful
Confident	Hard-working	Open-minded	Team-player
Conscientious	Helpful	Optimistic	Tenacious
Courageous	Honest	Organized	Thoughtful
Creative	Humble	Passionate	Tolerant
Curious	Imaginative	Patient	Trustworthy
Dependable	Industrious	Perceptive	Understanding
Diplomatic	Insightful	Personable	Upbeat
Direct	Integrity	Positive	Vibrant
Disciplined	Intelligent	Practical	Warm
Easygoing	Intuitive	Proactive	Wise
Enterprising	Inventive	Productive	

Once you have a list of your qualities, say them aloud with pride.

ENCOURAGE YOURSELF

Sometimes it can feel like the world is just waiting to knock us down. Encouraging ourselves helps us build a reserve of inner strength and resilience that can help us face whatever comes our way.

Since binge eating can be a way to cope with painful emotions, stress, or feeling like we're not good enough, encouragement shifts our mindset and makes us feel better. That positive responsiveness is a powerful tool in managing our emotions and ultimately, our relationship with food.

When we feel good about ourselves, we're less likely to turn to food for comfort or as a way to cope with life's challenges. So, giving yourself a pat on the back and cheering yourself on can really make a difference in overcoming binge eating.

Identify why you're feeling discouraged. What is the biggest obstacle you're facing?
(e.g., I can't lose weight, I'm worried about my health, I feel stuck in my marriage, I worry nothing is going to change.)

Imagine it's not you who's going through this struggle. Instead, it's your best friend, your partner, sibling, child, or someone you care about a lot. Write down everything you would say to your friend.

(e.g., I know you're having a difficult time and it's tough. I believe in you and I know things are going to get better. What can I do to help you?)

Now, write those things about your own situation. Hint: Want a shortcut? Change the pronouns of what you wrote to your friend. Replace "you" with "I" or "me" or "myself."

(e.g., I know I'm having a difficult time and it's tough. I believe in myself and I know things are going to get better. What can I do to help myself?)

Make a list of your accomplishments.

Make a list of challenges that you have overcome.

BABY YOURSELF

Babies aren't born hating their bodies. We learn to hate our bodies. We learn to hate ourselves. And, we can unlearn that and find a new way to relate to ourselves—body and mind. Let's hit the refresh button and go back to feeling as confident and happy as we were as babies.

Find one of your baby pictures or a photo of you as a very young child.

Write what the baby looks like.
(for example, cute chubby thighs, wide smile)

Write what the baby is thinking.
(e.g., I need a nap, I want to play, I want more attention)

What is the baby feeling?
(e.g., happy, sad, lonely, frightened, anxious)

What does the baby want/need?
(a hug, attention, a toy, to be left alone)

If you could go back in time, how would you take care of the baby or child?
(e.g., give cuddles and reassurance, make them feel safe and special).

How do you feel about that baby or child?
(e.g., loving, protective)

MAKE A CONTRACT WITH YOURSELF

Putting our promises to ourselves in writing makes our intentions more tangible, helps us process, and helps keep us accountable. Plus, when we see our goals and promises written out, it's easier to track our progress and celebrate our victories along the way.

By drafting up a contract with yourself, you're sending a message that you take your commitment to yourself seriously. You're ready to become the happiest version of yourself.

SAMPLE CONTRACT

Dear (Your Name) _____

I hereby promise that for the next (period of time) _____
I will nurture you in the following ways:

- ☐ *I will eat good healthy food when I am hungry*
- ☐ *I will notice and attend to whatever emotions I am feeling.*
- ☐ *I will feed my mind and do something I find interesting*
- ☐ *I will do something creative and fulfilling.*
- ☐ *I will get in touch with my spiritual side (if so inclined) by* _____

Make it your own. Add your intentions:

- ☐ _____
- ☐ _____
- ☐ _____

At minimum, when I am sad, lonely, or upset, I will connect with the following two people who I trust, like, or love:

_____

Love, (Your name)

GO ON A WORD DIET

You're probably familiar with the expression, "Sticks and stones can break my bones, but words can never hurt me." That's not true. Broken bones can mend and be almost like new again.

Words cause pain that never heals. Words weigh heavily on you. It's bad enough when someone else says hurtful things, but what about the way you talk to yourself? Here are seven words to eliminate from your vocabulary.

Fat

Can't

Dumb/Stupid/Idiot

Normal

Ridiculous

But

Should

What words do you use most often?
Choose one to eliminate from your vocabulary.

How did this impact your mood and self-esteem?

CHECK IN WITH YOURSELF

*What's your **happiness** today on a scale of 1—10? Why?*

*What's your **sadness** today on a scale of 1—10? Why?*

*What's your **anger** today on a scale of 1—10? Why?*

*What's your **anxiety** today on a scale of 1—10? Why?*

WHAT DO YOU WANT TO LOSE?

Do you imagine that when you lose weight, your life will improve, and you will be more confident, outgoing, and relaxed?

If so, you may think that by controlling the number on the scale, you can manage many aspects of your life, including your likability and lovability.

When weight symbolically represents the qualities you want to get rid of—such as shyness, insecurity, anxiety, etc.—losing weight becomes equivalent to losing unacceptable "parts" of yourself.

What are the "bad" parts of yourself that you want to get rid of?
(e.g., I hate that I'm shy and have so much self-doubt.)

THE SELF-LOVE ACTIVATORS: WHAT DO YOU WANT TO LOSE?

What do you imagine will be different if you are at a different weight?
(I'll be more confident and outgoing.)

How do you hope losing weight will change you as a person?
(I'll be more social and have lots of new friends.)

How did you come to believe those qualities are unacceptable?
(I never feel as if I quite fit in and it seems like everyone else is confident and outgoing.)

THE SELF-LOVE ACTIVATORS: WHAT DO YOU WANT TO LOSE?

What is a different way of thinking about the parts of yourself that you want to lose?

For example, many shy people have friends. Being quiet doesn't make me unlikable. It's possible that I notice people who are outgoing and assume they are confident and happy.

Having self-doubt is something lots of people struggle with, no matter what they weigh. Being outgoing doesn't equate to an absence of doubt.

There are areas in my life that I do feel confident about and I'll focus on them.

GOOD ENOUGH

Let's challenge the idea that you're not good enough as you are today, right now, this minute, whatever your place in life, no matter what you're doing or not doing, no matter what you weigh.

Describe a time when you didn't worry about food or your weight, and you felt carefree and happy.

What was going on in your life at the time?

What has changed since then?

What is the same?

Describe your ideas about what is "good enough" from your point of view.

Where did those standards come from?

Do you hold others to those standards?
Why? Why not?

BECOME AN OBSERVER

One way of being less self-conscious about your weight, eating in front of others, or any other aspect of your life is to **become an observer**. When the spotlight moves off you and onto the outside world, you'll be looking at the world instead of the world looking at you.

Step One: Look around. What do you see?
Notice as many visual details as possible about your environment. Whether you're in a conference room at the office or hanging out at home, look closely at the details around you. Note colors, textures, people, pets, cars, billboards, pictures, paintings, birds, and everything in sight.

Step Two: What do you hear?
Listen to the conversations around you. What is the content of the interactions? Are people talking about the world, themselves, or other people?

Step Three: What do you think?

Check in with yourself on whether you agree or disagree with what others are saying.

What are your thoughts about the opinions expressed in the conversations you are overhearing?

What are your observations about the people around you?

When you focus on what *you* think of other people and situations, you will
not feel like a target of their potentially critical thoughts about you.

THE POWER OF TEN

Settle down in a special space where you feel comfortable and rest for at least ten minutes. You can focus on breathing, listen to music, or do something else that is relaxing. Recall what you feel proud of and consider what you like about yourself and your evolution as a person.

At the end of your relaxation time, make a list of at least ten things (yes, TEN!) that you appreciate about yourself. It can be things you like about your body, personality, or life.

One	*Six*
Two	*Seven*
Three	*Eight*
Four	*Nine*
Five	*Ten*

THE FOOD FREEDOM IDENTIFIERS

Our past experiences can have a powerful influence on our present feelings and food habits. For many of us, being fed in our parent's arms was our first experience of love and comfort. So, when we're feeling vulnerable or in need of comfort, we may turn to food to reconnect with that feeling of safety and love.

Food is always there for us when we need it. People, on the other hand, can disappoint us, hurt us, or leave us. It can be easy to fall into a pattern of soothing ourselves with food when what we really need is comfort and support from another person.

Maybe you've had an experience in your past that left you feeling "not good enough." Those feelings of inadequacy can lead us to try to fill that emptiness with food.

Maybe you've had an experience in your past that left you feeling "not good enough." Those feelings of inadequacy can lead us to try to fill that emptiness with food.

Childhood experiences can really affect how we relate to ourselves and the world, and sometimes we end up eating for comfort instead of dealing with our emotions in a healthy way. The good news is that when we heal the past, we feel better in the present.

DO YOU FEEL GOOD ENOUGH?

Let's challenge the idea that you're not good enough as you are today, right now, this minute, whatever your place in life, no matter what you're doing or not doing, no matter what you weigh.

Describe a time when you didn't worry about food or your weight, and you felt carefree and happy.

What was going on in your life at the time?

What has changed since then?

THE FOOD FREEDOM IDENTIFIERS: DO YOU FEEL GOOD ENOUGH?

Describe your ideas about what is "good enough" from your point of view.

Where did those standards come from?

Think of some alternatives to those ideas.

GET COMFORTABLE WITH NEEDS & WANTS

We all need love, connection, attention, and comfort in our lives. But if those needs aren't met, or if they're met inconsistently, it makes us feel bad about having needs in the first place.

That's when we think of "needs" as "neediness," and it becomes something negative that we want to avoid. Binge eating is a way of saying, "I can't trust people to always be there for me, so I'll just turn to food instead. It's always there, it's consistent, and it helps fill up that empty feeling inside."

Make a list of your top three needs.

Now make a list of your top three wants.

How are you meeting those needs and wants?

What can you do to ensure you don't ignore them?

Are there ways that you can better express them?

What do you need more of in your life?

In what areas of your life do you feel deprived?

What's it like to think about your needs and wants?

HOW TO BE LESS ANXIOUS

What if I gain five pounds after eating that cookie/sandwich/pizza?

What if I go out with that guy and he turns out to be a complete jerk?

What if I ask someone out on a date and she rejects me?

What if I ask my boss for a raise and she gets mad?

What if I make a mistake and get fired?

What if I'm making the wrong choice?

What if I say the wrong thing?

"What if" is about fear, and has to do with believing that punishment, rejection, or deprivation lies ahead. When you have here-and-now emotions about future events, you may feel overwhelmed, which leads you into the kitchen.

In contrast, "what is" is about facts. It references what is known and true. When you are grounded in what is actually happening, or what you know to be true, you are less likely to feel anxious, worried, or upset.

What if = fear. What are you worried about that has to do with an imagined future?

What is = facts. What do you know right here, right now?
Who are you, right here, right now? What do you know to be true about yourself?

How have you handled difficult situations in the past?

Remembering who you are and recognizing your capabilities can
mitigate fear, because when you know you can get past difficult
situations, you are less afraid of them.

COOKIES DON'T CURE FEELINGS

I'll never forget the day I took my oldest daughter to the park and almost yelled at another mom. While my daughter was playing, I saw two toddlers, a boy and a girl, were playing in a sandbox, scooping sand into a pail. Suddenly, the boy ran off with the shovel.

The girl burst into tears. Her anxious mother ran up, saying, "Don't cry, don't cry, it's okay."

As the girl continued to bawl, her mother frantically reached into her bag, producing a box of animal crackers. "Here," she said, "Have a cookie."

That's when I wanted to yell at the mom, "What are you doing??" Because in that moment, the girl learned her feelings can upset others and she shouldn't have them or show them. But if she absolutely could not stop the feelings, a cookie would resolve the problem.

She would probably grow up thinking she had to suppress her emotions. And when she couldn't, she'd reach for cookies. Hello, emotional eating!

Other possible responses:

A *dismissive parent* might not notice that the child was crying or might glance over and say, "You're okay. It's not the end of the world." The child gets the message that her feelings are of no interest to others.

An *angry parent* might snap, "Stop crying already!" The child learns her feelings upset others.

A *supportive parent* might say, "Of course you're upset. It's okay to cry it out. That hurts your feelings." The girl feels soothed, understood, and comforted.

How do you speak to yourself when you are upset?
Are you anxious, dismissive, angry, or supportive?

Where did you learn to relate to yourself this way?

How do you soothe yourself when you're upset?

How do you soothe others?

DISAPPOINTMENT

I thought things would be different.

I feel so stupid for thinking it would work out.

I can't believe I trusted that person.

Paulette went into escrow on her dream house but the deal fell apart. She said, "I feel so stupid for thinking things would go my way. I can't believe I let myself get so excited about the house. I should have known better."

Instead of processing her disappointment about the house, Paulette attacked herself for failing to psychically know what would happen. Then, she comforted herself with ice cream.

When we process disappointment instead of turning it on ourselves, we stop using food to cope.

What is going on in your life that is causing disappointment?
Perhaps a friend has let you down, or other things have not gone as planned.

What does it mean about you?

Perhaps you fear that you're not good enough, not omniscient, that you somehow should have known better. If so, explore the meaning of powerlessness.

What does it mean about other people?
For example, you cannot trust others, that they are inherently self-serving and will throw you under the proverbial bus? If so, consider where you learned not to trust people.

What does it mean about the world?

For example, the world is an unfair, unsafe place and there are no rules. Bad things can happen to good people. Explore your life experiences to understand how you came to this belief.

What does it mean about the future?
For example, nothing is ever going to go your way and there's no point in trying or
trusting again. If so, examine your ideas about hopelessness.

ME, MYSELF & I

How you speak to yourself reveals a lot about your relationship to different aspects of yourself. There are usually three basic parts: the Self, the Critic, and the Soother/Supporter.

The "Self" refers to the part of you that has needs, wants, wishes, emotions, and conflicts. When you say, "I was feeling mad/sad/glad/afraid" that's your "Self" talking. Ideally, when you have a need, wish, emotion, or conflict, it's important to comfort or soothe yourself with kind words. If you criticize yourself instead, you might turn to food to escape your own mean voice.

And guess what? That leads the critic to judge you. If you say to yourself, "How could you have eaten that?" or "You failed!" you then may eat to get away from your own mean voice. It becomes a never-ending cycle.

But here's the thing: when you start responding to yourself in a gentle, soothing way instead of criticizing or attacking, you're less likely to binge or overeat. It's all about being kinder to yourself.

Let's challenge that "Critic" that informs you of all your perceived transgressions. It is relentlessly critical and able to find fault. (Hint: When you refer to yourself in the second person, it's usually the critic talking.)

Does your internal critic remind you of anyone you know?
Who spoke to you in that way?

The "Soother/Supporter" is the part that can be calm, understanding, and supportive. Often, that's the part that can show up for other people, but not for you. Consider how you express support for others. What if you spoke that way to yourself?

MISTAKES

I once discovered a typo on the "thank you" pop-up on my mailing list opt-in. Instead of "Welcome" it read "Wecome." Thousands of people had subscribed to the list, so THOUSANDS of people had seen the error.

Eeeek. Cringe. Total mortification.

When I confided what happened to a friend, she started to laugh. "I'm so relieved," she said. "You actually are human."

She told me that my error made me seem more accessible and fallible in her eyes, which from her perspective was a good thing. She also reminded me that all those subscribers still subscribed.

It's easy to lose perspective and feel as if a relatively minor mistake is huge. Worrying about a mistake can lead to negative self-talk and an expectation of perfectionism, both of which affect self-esteem.

When you feel bad about yourself, you're more likely to eat for comfort.

Let's change the meaning of mistakes.

What does it mean to make a mistake?

What do you feel when you've made an error?

What is your inner critic telling you?

What would you tell a friend in a similar situation?

How bad is the mistake in the overall scheme of things? The next time you make a mistake (which is part of life and therefore inevitable), keep this in mind:

Remember, you made a mistake. You are not a mistake.
Please give your perfectly-imperfect self a break!

SHOULD

One of my grad school professors said that the word "should" was the enemy of self-esteem. He said, "Don't 'should' on yourself" because it only creates a sense of shame.

The definition of "should" is: To express obligation or duty; also used to express expectation, conditionality. Yet, how many times have you told yourself:

I should not do that.

I should not have eaten that.

I shouldn't eat that.

I shouldn't want that.

I should be better at this.

I should get a better job.

I should have a boyfriend/girlfriend.

Often we speak to ourselves in second person, as if someone else is talking to us:

You shouldn't have eaten that.

You shouldn't have done that.

You shouldn't want that.

You should do better.

Whose voice does that sound like? How is it familiar?

The word "should" can cause us to direct anxiety, sadness, anger, and distress towards ourselves. Those feelings may be so powerful that we eat to cope.

What are the "should" thoughts that are causing you anxiety and upset?

Instead, ask yourself:

What do I want?

What am I feeling?

What's going on with me right now?

Be interested in your thoughts/emotions rather than judgmental!

ARE YOU A MIND READER?

When you walk into a room filled with strangers, what are your initial thoughts? Do you think the best? "These people are interested in me and can't wait to meet me!"

Or the worst? "These people think I'm fat... boring... stupid... etc." Believing other people are thinking the worst of you can be subtle, as in the following examples:

Arturo sat on the couch in my office, telling me about his weekend. He'd seen a couple of movies and spent time with his girlfriend. I nodded, listening. He sighed. "You're right, I should have done some work this weekend. I can't believe how lazy I am." Arturo's father always accused him of being a slacker, and he had internalized that view of himself. He thought I was viewing him through his father's eyes.

Corinne wept in frustration as she described a recent problem at work. She blew her nose and shook her head, apologetically. "You probably think I'm such a crybaby." Corinne grew up in a family that did not tolerate emotions or tears, which were viewed as signs of weakness. She imagined that I was viewing her tears contemptuously.

My friend *Kellie* and I had dinner and when she ordered dessert, she looked sheepish. "I know what you're thinking," she said. "I have no business eating tiramisu." Kellie's mother constantly monitored her weight, and Kellie automatically assumed I was, as well.

What do you think others are thinking about you?
Are they critical? Kind? Indifferent? Angry?

What is another way to view yourself and the situation?
What would you say to someone else in your position?
For example, "It's important to relax over the weekend and recharge your batteries" or
"It's healthy to cry if you're upset" or "It's okay to eat dessert, or anything, in moderation."

When you believe others are interested in you, rather than critical of you, you feel
less anxious/upset/guarded and are less likely to use food to cope.

EATING BECAUSE YOU'RE BORED

If you think you eat when you're bored, consider the possibility that something else may be going on. Boredom is about wanting to do something. To shake it off, you need to find an activity, get active, and be productive. Keep in mind that relying too much on being busy can stop you from really connecting with your thoughts and feelings.

Loneliness is a different story. It's all about wanting to be with someone. To beat loneliness, we need to spend time with others and build connections.

But emptiness? That's about feeling disconnected from yourself and what's going on inside you. Sometimes, you might feel bored when you're actually lonely or cut off from yourself. This can feel like emptiness or even show up as physical hunger. You might end up eating more to fill that symbolic emptiness inside you.

Do you turn to food instead of people?

What experiences have made you afraid to seek out or trust people?

*Does thinking about food give you something to "do" and distract
you from your thoughts and emotions?*

What would be most fulfilling to you right now?

When you're alone, what feelings are most uncomfortable?

How did you deal with these feelings as a child?

How did your family manage being busy, being alone, and being reflective?

HOW TO HANDLE HELPLESSNESS

Helplessness is a feeling that most people cannot bear to experience, either on its own or because it intensifies other painful or upsetting feelings. Helplessness is defined as: (1) unable to help oneself, (2) weak or dependent, (3) deprived of strength or power, (4) incapacitated. The state of helplessness is connected to vulnerability and dependency, both of which can be extremely uncomfortable. Anger, productivity, withdrawal and/or denial are ways of distracting from the intolerable state of helplessness.

ANGER

Anger is an active emotion, whereas helplessness is a passive emotion. You may get angry at yourself for your weight, or be upset with yourself for what you're eating, or the amount, as a way of avoiding your sense of helplessness.

How does this resonate with you?

PRODUCTIVITY

Being busy is another way of turning passive to active. Focusing on achievements, productivity, and being a slave-driver to yourself are all strategies to distract from helplessness. Thinking about food, weight, and calories are examples of focusing on "doing" rather than "feeling."

How do you relate to this?

WITHDRAWAL

Withdrawal is a way of denying helplessness.
That can mean a withdrawal from people, from
wants, and from needs.

How does this resonate?

DENIAL

If you tell yourself that what makes you feel helpless "isn't a big deal" you may be denying your true feelings in order to minimize the reality of the situation. This is a way of dismissing your feelings.

Explore how you may do this.

How do you feel helpless in your life? If you weren't feeling helpless over food, what would you feel helpless about?

If you weren't focused on being powerful over food and hunger,
what would you be focused on?

If you weren't trying to control food, what would you be trying to control?

CONTROL

"I was totally out of control with ice cream last week."
"I didn't eat anything all day. It felt good to be in control."
"I hate getting mad because I feel so out of control."

If you are struggling with food, it may seem as if the very thing you are trying to control (food, weight, and so forth) is actually controlling you.

Sometimes trying to control food can be a way of dealing with feelings of powerlessness in other parts of our lives. It's a lot easier to focus on what we eat or how much we weigh than to deal with an unpredictable boss, teacher, partner, or friend.

When we can't control someone else's behavior, we try to control ourselves instead. The desire to manage a person or situation ends up shifting to controlling our food.

Controlling things can also be a way to protect ourselves from feeling vulnerable. Being vulnerable can make us feel like we're wide open to emotional pain.

What parts of your life make you feel powerless? Powerful?

Who is (or was) the most controlling person in your life?

What do you associate with weakness?

What are you afraid will happen if you lose control of your emotions?

Have you ever "lost it" emotionally? What were the consequences?

What are your fears about opening up to other people?

Where did you learn to be guarded?

"COMPARISON IS THE THIEF OF JOY."

~ Theodore Roosevelt

It's so easy to get caught up in comparing ourselves to others, whether it's on social media, at work, or even within our own circle of friends.

The problem is, when we constantly measure our worth against others, or our appearance to others, we end up focusing on what we lack rather than appreciating what we have. This can lead to feelings of inadequacy and rob us of our happiness.

Where did you get the idea that you're not as good as others?

What do you think needs to change? Weight? Marital status? Financial status?

What makes you think that depriving yourself (dieting) reflects strength of character?

Think of someone you compare yourself to unfavorably. What do you imagine would change if you had her (or his) looks, weight, or life?

What aspects of yourself—physical, intellectual, mental,
emotional—do you feel good about?

What makes you happy?

TRY A LITTLE MAGIC

If only my "magic wand" worked the way Harry Potter's does in books and movies! I could wave it over you and instantly heal your relationships to yourself.

I would replace self-criticism with self-acceptance and help you process feelings instead of turning on yourself, using food/weight as a weapon.

Alas, the magic wand doesn't work instantly. But here's the good news: we all have the power to change, to identify patterns and destructive attitudes and to react and act differently.

We have our own magic within us. We can heal ourselves with a combination of insight, hope, tenacity, reflection, courage, and more. Binge eating or focusing on food often distracts from deeper fears and conflicts. When you work through these concerns, you no longer need food to cope.

I've been told that my wand actually does work... just slowly. So, imagine if in a wave of this wand, I could stop all thoughts of food, weight, calories, fat grams, or anything connected to eating, weight, or body image.

If these concerns no longer occupied your mind, what would you think about?

FEAR OF ABANDONMENT

Concern that others will leave you and that you'll be alone.

Is this a familiar concern? If so, what comes to mind?

FEAR OF REJECTION

Concern that other people will judge you and won't like you.

When is the first time you remember feeling this way?

What else comes to mind?

FEAR OF PUNISHMENT

Fear that you'll get in trouble or be punished in some way.

Write your thoughts about this.

Focusing on food can distract from these deeper anxieties. Yet, when you identify
and process them, you stop eating for distraction or comfort, and you feel more
comfortable with yourself, your body, and others.

WHAT DO YOU WANT TO LOSE?

I need to lose 10/20/50/100 pounds.

These thighs have got to go.

I can't wait to get rid of this flab.

The $60 billion diet industry sells us the illusion that if we just lose weight our lives will be better, and we'll be more confident, outgoing, and relaxed.

If that sounds familiar, you might think that controlling the number on the scale will help you manage other parts of your life, like how likable or lovable you are.

Your weight starts to symbolize all the things you want to change about yourself—shyness, insecurity, anxiety, and so on—and shedding those pounds feels like you're shedding those unwanted parts of yourself.

But that is an illusion. Focusing on weight can be a distraction. It's easier to think about losing weight than it is to think about shedding disappointments, fears, concerns, worries, and anxieties.

What are the "bad" parts of yourself that you want to get rid of?

What do you imagine will be different if you are at a different weight?

How do you imagine losing weight will change you as a person?

*What qualities about yourself (not physical characteristics)
do you think you need to get rid of? Why?*

How did you come to believe those qualities are unacceptable?

SELF-CARE MASTERY PRESCRIPTIONS

The goal of self-care is to create a sense of balance and overall health, which helps you cope with whatever life throws your way. Practicing regular self-care helps you feel better in your day-to-day life and also makes you more resilient when things aren't going so well.

When we're confident in our ability to take care of ourselves, and when we feel worthy of that care, we don't use food or any other negative coping strategy to cope.

Some people find that meditation brings them inner peace. Others prefer physical activities like running, walking, hiking, or working out. Self-care can also mean quiet time, reading a book, watching a good show, or journaling. Self-care looks different for everyone, but it is always about refocusing and reconnecting with all the different parts of yourself.

When we're confident in our ability to take care of ourselves, and when we feel worthy of that care, we don't use food or any other negative coping strategy to cope.

WHAT IS SELF-CARE, ANYWAY?

"I'm the queen of self care," said Hildy. "So why am I bingeing?"

Hildy got regular manicures and pedicures, massages, facials, and weekly blowouts for her hair. Yet, she still struggled with feelings of depression and worthlessness. She wondered why she still felt so bad, since she was taking such good care of herself.

What she didn't realize is that true self care is more than just grooming (which is what she was doing). Self-care means taking care of yourself in all areas of life. It means considering what you want and need, which can be different for everyone.

Taking care of yourself is a way of recognizing that you're worthy of care and attention. The goal of self-care is to build resilience and create a balance in our lives, which helps us cope with the challenges of life. The more we do that, the less we turn to other ways of coping, such as binge eating or emotional eating.

Here are some examples of self-care:

Emotional self-care:

Writing in a journal or practicing other forms of self-reflection

Self-reflection: Regularly taking time to reflect on your emotions and experiences can help you identify patterns and work through difficult feelings

Seeking support from a therapist, counselor, or support group (we need others to help us through difficulties)

Practicing self-compassion and encouraging self-talk

Mental self-care:

Taking breaks from work or other responsibilities to give your mind a rest

Engaging in activities that you find mentally stimulating, such as puzzles, drawing, reading or learning something new

Seeking out new experiences and learning opportunities for intellectual growth

Having fun, whether that means watching a great TV show, playing a game, or other fun activities

Physical self-care:

Ensuring you get enough sleep and rest

Getting regular exercise or doing outdoor activities

Taking breaks throughout the day to stretch, walk, work out, or move your body in some way

Spiritual Self-Care:

Connecting with spirituality

Cultivating a sense of purpose (which can include practicing meditation, attending religious services, or engaging in other practices that help foster a sense of meaning in life).

Social Self-Care:

Building a supportive network of friends and family

Connecting with a community by participating in groups, clubs, and/or organizations

Taking breaks from social media to be with others

What does self-care mean to you? How do you define it?

How do you prioritize self-care in your life? Do you prioritize it enough?

SELF-CARE MASTERY PRESCRIPTIONS: WHAT IS SELF-CARE, ANYWAY?

What self-care practices do you currently have in your life? How do they make you feel?

What are some small ways you can practice self-care every day?

What are your barriers to practicing self-care?

What is one step you can take to overcome them?

How do you feel about asking for help when it comes to self-care? Why?

What makes you feel drained and depleted?

What activities make you feel calm and relaxed?

SELF-CARE ISN'T SELFISH

Selfishness is an attitude or behavior that prioritizes someone's own needs and desires over the needs and desires of others. Selfish people act in ways that benefit themselves, and don't think about how their actions impact others—often they don't care. Selfish people have an attitude of, "What's the world doing for me, lately?" rather than considering how they affect others.

The opposite of selfishness is being too selfless, which is also detrimental. Being overly selfless refers to neglecting your own needs and well-being in order to prioritize the needs of others. While selflessness is generally seen as a positive trait in certain contexts, when taken to an extreme, it can lead to neglecting yourself.

It is important to find a balance between being selfless and taking care of your own needs in order to maintain overall health and well-being. When we take care of ourselves, we're better able to cope with stress and manage our emotions. We're also able to be more present for the people in our lives. Self-care isn't selfish—it's actually one of the most important things you can do for yourself and also for others.

Do you feel selfish when you take care of yourself? Why?

What evidence do you have that you are being selfish? Are you neglecting the needs of others, or simply taking care of yourself?

Where did you learn to put the needs of others before your own?
Perhaps it was modeled for you or expected of you. Write your thoughts.

How will taking care of yourself ultimately benefit you and those around you? Think of how you'll be better able to show up for others if you're rested, relaxed, and fulfilled.

How can you set healthy boundaries and communicate your needs clearly?

What activities nourish your mind, body, and soul?

Pick one activity and commit to doing it in the next week. Write it here:

SELF-CARE MASTERY PRESCRIPTIONS: SELF-CARE ISN'T SELFISH

Taking care of yourself doesn't have to be a major undertaking. Even small, simple actions can make a positive impact on your well-being. Take some time for you today—that might mean taking a few deep breaths or going for a quick walk outside.

Try prioritizing self-care realistically, even if it means carving out five or ten minutes a day or an hour a week. Try experimenting to find what works best for you.

Describe what this was like for you.

FIND YOUR OXYGEN

When you travel on a plane, flight attendants tell passengers, *"Parents, if the oxygen masks drop, place a mask over yourself first before attending to your children."*

This underscores the importance of self-care. When you give your oxygen away, you deprive yourself of air and suffocate. Similarly, when you take care of others and deplete yourself, you may use food to meet those unmet needs.

What is your "oxygen?" What are you depriving yourself of (but giving away to others)?

What do you need more of in your life?

How do you make yourself available to others?

Do you let others take care of you? If so, what does that stir up in you?
If not, what stops you?

When you were growing up, what were you taught about self-sacrifice? (e.g., was it noble?)

SELF-CARE MASTERY PRESCRIPTIONS: FIND YOUR OXYGEN

Here are ten activities that feed your mind, body, and/or soul. Pick one to do today, another to do tomorrow, and a third to do the following day.

Talking with a friend
Exercising
Reading a good book
Getting a massage

Going to the movies
Playing with your kids/grandkids/
    nieces/nephews
Meditating

Taking a dog for a walk
Drinking a cup of tea
Listening to music
Watching your favorite TV show

Today I will:

Tomorrow I will:

The next day I will:

SHARE YOUR STRUGGLE

"Troubles shared are troubles halved."

When we open up and share our troubles, we receive understanding and support, which makes us feel better. Sharing is caring. The first step is to identify what stops you from sharing.

Are you afraid you will burden others? Do you think their opinion of you will change? Are you embarrassed?

Today, you will call/email/text a friend and talk about something that's bothering you or something that's on your mind.

I commit to phoning (or emailing or texting) the following person:	
I'm going to share:	*If I get nervous, I will keep in mind:*

The more you do this, the more connected and fulfilled you are in your relationships,
the less empty you will feel, and the less likely you are to use food to fill that void.

Sharing with others alleviates whatever is "weighing" on you.
Share something today. Take action now!

STOP-THE-SABOTAGE CLARIFIERS

Does this happen to you? You finally see results and you're thrilled. The scales are moving in the right direction, and your clothes are feeling a little looser. You're so close to your goal weight...it's so exciting!!

And then something happens. You binge on ice cream, cookies, and cake. You can't understand why you're doing this. It makes no sense and you're frustrated with yourself. It seems you'll never stop this cycle.

There is hope. One of the main reasons we sabotage our success is because of fear. We can become comfortable with feeling uncomfortable because at least we know what to expect. Familiarity is safe.

One of the main reasons we sabotage our success is because of fear. We can become comfortable with feeling uncomfortable because at least we know what to expect. Familiarity is safe.

If you repeatedly sabotage your success, it's time to take a good hard look at yourself and your beliefs. Do you fear change? Maybe you have some expectation of yourself at a lower weight. Or perhaps you worry you won't be able to maintain your success.

Once you identify the root cause of your self-sabotage, you can break free from it. Don't let your fears hold you back any longer! When you stop the sabotage, you won't have to worry about willpower or control, and you'll enjoy true liberation.

CLARIFY YOUR OBSTACLES

Mark the phrases that you identify with the most (check all that apply):

Category #1

☐ I'm afraid I'll leave my spouse/partner

☐ I'll change my job or career

☐ I'll become a different person (e.g., impulsive, spontaneous, etc.)

☐ I'll do something unpredictable

Category #2

☐ I'll feel like a thing and not a person

☐ I will have too much excess skin

☐ I don't know what I'll look like as a thinner person

☐ People won't care about me as a person

Category #3

☐ When I lose weight, I'll finally start dating (but what if I don't find someone?)

☐ When I lose weight, I'll find a better job (but what if I can't keep it?)

☐ When I lose weight, I'll have kids (but what if I'm a bad parent?)

☐ When I lose weight, I'll travel (but what if I pick the wrong place to go?)

Category #4

☐ I won't be able to keep off the weight

☐ Something bad is going to happen to me

☐ I'm not meant to have good things

☐ I'm afraid that I will mess it up

Write down how many phrases you marked in each category.

Category #1 _____

Category #3 _____

Category #2 _____

Category #4 _____

Category #1

FEAR OF IMPULSIVITY

This is a fear that losing weight will cause you to be impulsive, spontaneous, and unpredictable in some major area of your life, such as your relationship or career. You may also be concerned about hurting other people or disrupting their lives if you make changes.

What do you want more of in life?

What do you think you will do if you lose weight?

What would you focus on if you were not thinking about your weight or food?

Category #2

FEAR OF OBJECTIFICATION

Weight can serve as a shield to protect you from other people. One of my patients once poignantly said, "Bad things don't happen to fat girls."

People with negative experiences with intimacy often fear being objectified, treated as a body or a thing rather than as a person. In the absence of satisfying and fulfilling connection with people, food becomes a substitute. Unlike people, food is consistent, available, and reliable.

What makes you nervous or afraid of romantic attention?

What are your associations to intimacy, closeness, and to being in a relationship?

What do you fear will happen if you're perceived as attractive to others?

Category #3

FEAR OF EXPECTATION

People often believe that once they lose weight, a new boyfriend, girlfriend, job and/or career will magically appear. The diet industry sells the idea that our personalities will change when we lose weight.

If we're insecure, we'll become confident. If we're shy, we'll become outgoing. Sounds good, right?

Only, it's an illusion. And the hidden fear is, what if that does not happen? What if everything in life stays exactly the same, except for the label size on our clothes?

We cannot resolve psychological conflicts or anxieties by changing our bodies. You may feel good about your weight loss, but you will not suddenly become a different person. You will be yourself, just lighter.

What qualities about yourself (not physical characteristics) do you think you need to get rid of?

How did you come to believe those qualities are unacceptable?

What do you imagine would be different if you were at a different weight?

Category #4

FEAR OF FAILURE

Fear of failure has to do with your identity and sense of self. Keep in mind that there is a difference between "failing" and "being a failure." Failing has to do with achievement, with what you're doing or not doing. Being a failure has to do with you as a person.

When your definition of "failure" goes beyond the fact of failing to achieve a goal and takes on the meaning of being a failure as a person, that may feel unbearable.

It can be easier not to put much effort into losing weight or being healthy, which pretty much guarantees failure, than it is to feel terrible if you try really hard and don't meet your goal.

If fear of failure is keeping you stuck, then confront the idea that you are a failure if you fail. Learn to consider yourself a person who has tried and failed, not a failure as a person. And be sure to congratulate yourself for having the courage to tackle tough challenges.

What were the messages you got about success and failure as a child?

What does failure say about you?

How do you support yourself in difficult times?

ARE YOU SCARED TO BE SKINNY?

The first three years of Rosalind's life were absolutely ideal. Her grandmother took care of her while her parents were at work. She consistently felt loved and secure. Then, two events took place: first, her grandmother fell ill and was no longer able to care for Rosalind, and soon after, a baby brother was born.

Suddenly, instead of feeling safe and secure with her familiar grandmother, Rosalind spent her days adjusting to daycare and her nights feeling neglected, since her parents were preoccupied with the newborn and could not focus solely on her, as they had previously. Rosalind had been a happy, outgoing child but she soon became anxious and unsettled. She soothed herself with snacks, a habit that carried with her into adulthood.

Rosalind and I noticed that her binges intensified after she got a promotion at work. She attributed it to increased job pressure, but I wondered if something else was going on.

Was Rosalind afraid of happiness? Rosalind's early experiences taught her that she couldn't trust good times. Her grandmother's illness and brother's birth followed a period of childhood bliss, so she interpreted that blissful time as a set-up for loss.

If she never allowed herself to feel "too good" she would never step onto the rug of happiness, only to have it yanked out from beneath her. One way to ensure she didn't feel "too" happy was to always be upset about her weight.

You may have a belief (conscious or unconscious) that by daring to be happy, you're inviting punishment from the universe. By never feeling good about your weight, you control the unhappy aspects of life, rather than waiting for it to come out of the blue.

What are your fears about happiness?

What are your hopes?

Do you have a sense that things are "too good to last" when life is going well?

Where did you get the message that happiness can't last?

STOP THE SABOTAGE: ARE YOU SCARED TO BE SKINNY?

Do you attach a positive meaning to unhappiness? For example, some people hold the idea that it's noble to struggle, that suffering makes you a better person.

STOP THE SABOTAGE: ARE YOU SCARED TO BE SKINNY?

Think of something that brought you a sense of peace, wellbeing, happiness, or joy.

What prevents you from holding onto that feeling?

When you allow yourself to trust the idea that happiness can last, you'll allow
yourself to get to a weight that you're happy with—and stay there.

STOP THE FAT TALK

The way you talk about yourself affects the way you feel about yourself. When you are filled with self-loathing you are vulnerable to using food to cope.

That's why it's important to cultivate some DOs and DON'Ts about the way you talk about yourself. Do NOT compare your body to others. Never. Ever.

Do NOT say anything bad about your body. That means not talking about the size of your thighs, the shape of your stomach, nose, knees, or any other body part.

DO find positive physical attributes to focus on. We tend to find the evidence we're looking for, so if you look for physical qualities you like about yourself, you WILL find them (I promise!).

Here are some examples:

Nice eyes	Nice smile	Great hair	Eyebrows
Smooth skin	Strong legs	Beautiful lips	Hourglass
White teeth	Strong arms	Bone structure	Shape
Height			

Write five things you appreciate about your appearance.

Challenge the idea that you will be happier when you are thinner.

Write three reasons why your size is not tied to your happiness or well-being.

DO identify what would be on your mind if you were not focused on your body. Fat talk can distract you from deeper troubles. Fat talk distracts you from what's going on inside that needs your attention.

Write down your anxieties.

Identify what is aggravating or causing you to be angry.

What are you sad about right now?

DO focus on having a healthy body, not a perfect body.

DO assess the size of your heart, not the size of your jeans.

DO remember, "fat is a substance, not a feeling."

Losing weight takes time, but you can drop the fat talk and feel better in no time!

MIRROR MIRROR

Go to the nearest mirror and look at your reflection. Say aloud, "I accept you."

Guess what? You are NOT going to suddenly and magically like your reflection!

Affirmations don't work in the long run. Why? Because although there may be a conscious, logical and rational part of your mind that finds yourself acceptable and lovable, another part of your mind—a more powerful part of you—believes the opposite.

This mirror exercise brings those unconscious thoughts into conscious awareness, so you can begin challenging them.

When you say, "I accept myself" what does the internal naysayer think?

STEP ONE

Write down your automatic responses to the "I accept you" affirmation.
Examples:
You're too fat/old/young/tall/short
Nobody will ever find you attractive
You can't do anything right
I'm not good enough
I'm not where I'm supposed to be in life

STEP TWO

Where did these ideas come from? Are they based on an interpretation of your circumstances? What comes to mind?

Examples:

People have rejected me, so there must be something wrong with me

I have not had a successful romantic relationship, so it must be me

I don't look like anyone in social media, so there's something wrong with my looks

I don't really fit in, so it must be me who's not good enough

All my friends are married and I have yet to meet someone, so I'm a weirdo

By this age, I should have achieved more at work

STEP THREE

Identify your strengths and all the qualities you like about yourself.

Examples:

I'm compassionate

I am open-minded

I respect others

I have beautiful eyes

I have strong legs

I work hard

STEP FOUR

Challenge the automatic negative thoughts with a different perspective.

Examples:

Being likable and lovable is not size-specific

I am a good, kind and interesting person and have yet to meet the right person

I have failed at things and succeeded at things; both are possible

I am good at lots of things

I don't look like anyone else because I am unique and special

My path is my own and I'm going at my own pace

When you recognize and accept your true self and challenge your negative assumptions, you can embrace a more realistic view of yourself. That balanced view is the key to self-acceptance!

If you don't have enough fun in your life, eating may be your one source of fun. The more you cultivate other forms of enjoyment and pleasure in your life, the less you'll use food for that purpose.

Have some fun!

HOW TO HAVE FUN BY YOURSELF

Take yourself to the movies—watch anything you want to see and sit anywhere you want!

Browse at a bookstore.

Watch your favorite TV series or find a new one. Binge-watching a show is a good kind of binge!

Watch people at a mall or at a park. Make up stories about their lives. Are they on their first date? Have they been married forever? What's their story?

Learn how to crochet or knit. You can learn on YouTube for free.

Do a crossword puzzle, Sudoku, or play Scrabble or chess with the computer.

Go to a park and swing on the swings, soaring as high as you dare.

Get creative—draw or paint, with a brush, charcoal, pen, pencil, or even do some finger painting!

Watch the sunset or the sunrise.

Volunteer to be a dog walker at a local dog rescue center (this could be so much fun that you might not go home alone!).

Pick one fun action that you commit to doing today:

And tomorrow: And the next day: And the next:

HOW TO HAVE FUN WITH FRIENDS OR FAMILY

Go to a karaoke bar and sing your heart out (or watch others). So fun and funny!

Take a dance or fitness class together.

Go to the zoo.

Play a board game—you might even start a regular Game Night.

Go on a walk, a hike or ride a bike.

Have an "ugly gift" party and vote on whose gift is the ugliest.

Plan a TV or movie marathon—pick a goofy theme that everyone enjoys.

Pick one fun action that you commit to doing today:

And tomorrow: And the next day: And the next:

Take action now! And have fun!!

OPPOSITE DAY

If your comfort zone has become your rut zone, it's time to do something different. In at least one of the following areas, try doing the opposite of what you usually do.

Career/job/business:

If you don't like to talk in meetings—speak up!

If you prefer to do a lot of talking—try listening instead.

If you tend to avoid leadership positions—try leading a committee or project.

If you prefer to work independently—try working with others on a project.

If you like to be one of many—dare to stand out and take on a solo project.

Family:

If you often let other family members make decisions about what movie to see, where to go to dinner or to vacation—be the decider.

If you avoid conflict—take action and confront a problem directly.

If your family members eat at different times—try a family meal.

Financial:

If you have no savings or retirement plan—start one.

If you save but never spend—buy something you want but don't need.

If you can't remember the last time you balanced your checkbook—do it!

Personal Development:

If you always wanted to learn a new language, or go horseback riding, or take ice skating lessons—sign up for those lessons.

If you can't imagine life without technology—take a walk without your phone, tablet or computer

Health:

If you only exercise at home—check out the local gym or YMCA (they usually offer one day passes for a reasonable fee).

If you put off making doctor or dentist appointments—call now.

If you always eat at fast food places or restaurants—try cooking instead.

If you are always on a rigid diet—relax your food rules.

Social:

If you are shy—try smiling at a stranger.

If you are single and have never tried online dating—create a profile and sign up.

If you only meet potential partners online—ask a friend to set you up on a date.

If you only date people with dark hair—try dating a redhead or a blonde.

If you only date tall people (or short people)—try going out with someone who doesn't meet your height requirements.

If you hate large gatherings—go to one and see what happens.

If you like parties with tons of people—have a few friends over for a small gathering.

THE DREAM LIFE ROADMAP: OPPOSITE DAY

Write about your hopes and fears before you took the opposite action.

What was the experience actually like? What surprised you?

What's your takeaway?

BALANCE YOUR LIFE!

Goals are great—but if you're always looking to the future, you're never truly in the present. If you're living in the past, you also miss what's happening in the present.

Imagine standing on a symbolic ladder that represents your life.

Look down the rungs. The lower rungs represent your past. Think about where you started in various areas of your life and recognize how far you've come.

Consider your experiences since you started this climb, recognizing the personal growth and evolution that brought you to this rung of your ladder.

Take a moment to appreciate your progress in relationships to others, relationship to yourself, in your career, and your evolution as a person.

RELATIONSHIP TO YOURSELF

How has it changed?

What do you want it to be?

What do you like about yourself right now?

RELATIONSHIP TO OTHERS

How have your relationships changed?

What improvements or changes do you seek in the future?

What do you like about your relationships right now?

CAREER / JOB

What has changed?

What do you want it to be?

What do you enjoy about your career right now?

When you balance appreciating your progress from the past with creating goals for the future and appreciating where you are in life at this moment, you will feel better about yourself and your life. Creating balance feeds your soul and helps you find inner peace!

MOVE YOUR BODY

Exercise has been shown to decrease both depression and anxiety. Moving your body also reduces stress and increases self-esteem. Commit to some kind of movement or exercise for a minimum of 10 minutes today. Ten minutes is doable. You've got this!

Here are some options:

Go on a walk

Take the stairs

Put on music and dance

Go on a hike

Jogging

Yoga

Mat Pilates

Tai chi

Water aerobics

Karate

Running

Jumping jacks

Gardening

Roller-skating

Hip Hop dance

Ballroom dance

Jazz dance

Salsa dance

Zumba dance

Rollerblading

Ice skating

Riding a bike

Lifting weights

Swimming

Cardio funk

Spinning

Horseback riding

Whatever form of physical movement you choose, allow yourself to appreciate the strength in your muscles, the beat of your heart, and allow yourself to feel truly alive.

Moving your body is good for your body and it's also good for your soul.

HOW TO CALM DOWN

By now you know it's important to identify and process your feelings so you don't turn to food when you're upset. But sometimes we're just too stressed out to deal with our emotions.

Here are some ways to alleviate stress and anxiety by centering your mind and stopping the escalation of stress.

PROGRESSIVE MUSCLE RELAXATION EXERCISE

Step One: Find a quiet place where you can be alone. Eventually you can do this exercise anywhere, but while learning the technique, it's helpful to practice alone.

Step Two: Create muscle tension in specific areas of your body. Start with your head and work downward (or start with your feet and go upward).

Squeeze your muscles as tightly as you can for as long as you can. HOLD that tension as long as possible, a minimum of ten seconds but ideally as long as possible.

Forehead: raise your eyebrows as far up as you can
Eyes: clench shut
Shoulders: lift towards your ears
Back: arch your back
Stomach: tighten your abs and pull in your abdominal muscles
Arms: tighten your biceps by making fists and squeezing hard
Legs: tighten your thighs
Feet: curl your toes downward

Step Three: Allow yourself to completely relax, releasing the tension from your muscles and enjoying the sensation.

Feel that? (wow, it feels so great, doesn't it?)

When you are relaxed, you are less likely to use food as a sedative.

The idea of this exercise is that without muscle tension, you can't access muscle release. When your body is relaxed, your mind will follow.

THE FOUR SENSES EXERCISE

We do have five senses, but if you turn to food when you're stressed, you're familiar with the sense of taste and probably use taste—food—as the primary way you self-soothe.

The Four Senses exercise puts you in touch with the other four senses and helps you center yourself. Wherever you are, look around and say one thing that you can:

Touch:
See:
Hear:
Smell:

Write about the experience in as much detail as possible.

VISUALIZATION

There are two ways to use visualization: the first is to imagine a happy place where you feel safe and calm; the second is to think about something you're afraid of, and imagine a positive outcome. Keep in mind those four senses.

Visualization #1: Visualize a place where you feel happy. Where are you? Who else is there? Don't limit yourself to reality; you can go anywhere your mind takes you. In your imagination, what are you touching, seeing, hearing, and smelling? *Visualization #2:* Imagine a situation that makes you nervous, thinking about the best outcome possible. Again, use the four senses to bring this to life.

What upcoming situation is causing you anxiety? Whether it's a job interview, a personal challenge, a blind date or anything else, imagine the very best outcome, visualizing and using the four senses.

Write about the experience in as much detail as possible.

CREATE A VISION BOARD

Step One: Get your supplies. You'll need the following:
Poster Board (available at FedEx, RiteAid, CVS, Target, and art supply stores)
Alternatively, break down a large cardboard box and use it.
Magazines
Newspapers
Photos
Scissors
A glue stick, thumbtacks

Step Two: Look through all the photos, magazines, and newspapers. Cut out, or tear out, anything that strikes you—headlines, articles, and anything that grabs your attention. Or find images online. Trust that an intuitive part of you is picking the right images.

Step Three: Divide everything into categories by theme, such as relationships, job, vacation, future, relaxation. If you have any doubts or reservations about anything you picked, put it aside. Again, trust yourself to pick what's right for you.

Step Four: Start gluing! The rule for this step is that there are no rules! Glue everything onto the board in whatever way that feels right. Allow yourself to go into a creative zone and feel free to be as whimsical or organized as you want.

Optional: Leave a space in the center of the board for a photo of yourself.

Step Five: Put the vision board where you can see it daily.
Ask yourself:
What goals am I close to achieving?
What goals have I already achieved?
What actions am I taking toward those goals (this journal counts toward an action)?

Creating a visual depiction of your ideal life helps by clarifying your goals, which is the first step towards making those dreams into realities.

♥

CONGRATULATIONS!

Congratulations!! You did it! I'm proud of you and I hope you're also really proud of yourself, because know this: it takes courage and dedication to complete this journal.

It can be easier to focus on what you're eating than on what's eating "at" you. You didn't take the easy way. You did the hard work of looking inward.

What have you achieved?

You cracked the code of emotional eating and discovered the real triggers to overeating or bingeing. You started seeing yourself and others in a new way and began expressing yourself in words instead of using food to cope.

You became a better friend to yourself by encouraging and inspiring yourself. Now, you know yourself better, can appreciate and acknowledge yourself, and you're having more fun.

You stopped the fat talk—that negative voice that makes you feel bad about yourself—and you learned to challenge that inner critic. You created a very specific vision for your future and clarified the goals that will help you achieve it.

And although you're at the end of this journal, I'm still here for you on your journey. Please join my Dr. Nina's "Food For Thought" Community on Facebook. I'm there to give you information and inspiration. Connect with others who "get it" and find support and motivation.

Again, congratulations on opening your mind and your heart to a new way of thinking about your relationship to food and to yourself.

Welcome to liberation, and a binge-free happy life!

—Dr Nina

Made in the USA
Middletown, DE
15 December 2023

45774439R00124